The EPA calls indoor air pollution *"America's most serious environmental problem affecting the health of humans."* Your home, for instance, has house dust. "Harmless enough," you say. *"Let's just vacuum it out."* Well, it doesn't work that way.

In this "harmless dust" are *thousands* of human skin flakes with thousands *more* of other ingredients mixed in, including: pet dander, gaseous components from cigarettes, cooking and fireplace smoke, industrial pollution, mold and yeast spores, dust mites (and their feces) outgassed chemicals from paints, glues from particle board and—the list goes on.

More than **50 million Americans** suffer from allergies, many of which are caused by INDOOR air pollutants. With most of the others, their allergies are AGGRAVATED by indoor air pollutants. For those who know about this stuff, it's frightening. And I'm hoping you do something about it—NOW!

To those that *don't,* this will be a grand awakening for you. Find out more on HOW to rid your home of these pollutants quickly, safely, inexpensively and forever. This book gives you the facts and the answers.

THE SILENT KILLER

INDOOR AIR POLLUTION

by

PETE BILLAC

SWAN PUBLISHING

Author: Pete Billac
Editor: Kimberly Newell
Cover Design: John Gilmore
Layout Design: Sharon Davis

RECENT BOOKS BY PETE BILLAC:

The Annihilator
How Not To Be Lonely
How Not To be Lonely—TONIGHT
The Last Medal of Honor
All About Cruises
New Father's Baby Guide
Willie the Wisp
Managing Stress
The New Millionaires

THE SILENT KILLER
1st printing - December 1999
2nd printing - February 2000

Copyright @ December 1999
Swan Publishing
Library of Congress Catalog Card #99-68643
ISBN# 0-943629-44-6

The Silent Killer, is available in quantity discounts through SWAN Publishing, 126 Live Oak, Alvin, TX 77511. Call at: (281) 388-2547, Fax (281) 585-3738 or e-mail: swanbooks@ghg.net
Printed in the United States of America.

INTRODUCTION

I enjoy writing and helping people. When I find a subject that will benefit others (and sell) I write about it. I, like many of you, only "heard" about the effect polluted air can have on our bodies and decided to find out more. I searched the Internet for information and what I discovered actually scared me.

The more I read about sicknesses that are associated with *indoor air pollution* it meant that it is a *major problem* and I began serious research on it. I found books and gathered pamphlets, looked for programs on TV and talked with various engineers and environmentalists about it.

I discovered that only THREE PERCENT of all the homes and businesses in North America have *any* type of air purification, but within the next two decades over NINETY PERCENT **WILL** have some type of system to purify the air. A *red flag* went up. This meant that this was a problem NOW—why are we waiting?

This means, if what I've been reading about was true, that EIGHTY-SEVEN percent of the people in the United States will suffer from allergies, headaches and watery eyes and other illnesses until they DO get these systems in their homes and offices and plants.

According to the *Department of Consumer Affairs*, CHILDREN and THE ELDERLY are especially adversely affected by polluted INDOOR air and they can do little about it. We can! Everybody, it would seem, would want the best protection for their kids, their parents and grandparents. I **WOULD!**

As I continued my research about this indoor air pollution problem, still MORE alarming facts hit me between the eyes. *The American College of Allergists* **avow** that 50% (HALF) of all illnesses are caused by polluted INDOOR air. They say that 10 to 12 MILLION Americans suffer from asthma, and that asthma is the SINGLE LARGEST CAUSE of hospital visits by children!

In this age of health and forcing cigarette smokers into near-isolation, The *American Lung Association* reports that over 20% of all ADULT Americans are cigarette smokers. There are no statistics on kids, because too many kids hide this fact from their parents.

Yet *another* frightening statistic, according to the *World Health Organization*, is that FORTY PERCENT of ALL BUILDINGS pose a "serious health hazard" due to indoor air pollution. And, Legionnaire's Disease continues to claim lives each year.

As I stated on page one, I don't mean to frighten you, but if it takes getting you a bit *shaken up*—scared even—to recognize this problem and to act, I'll be happy. More so, you and your family will be less likely to get sick.

TABLE OF CONTENTS

Chapter 1
THINGS IN YOUR HOUSE 9

Chapter 2
A SOLUTION? 21

Chapter 3
SICK BUILDING SYNDROME 31

Chapter 4
UNDERSTANDING CLEAN AIR 37

Chapter 5
IONS AND IONIZATION 42

Chapter 6
THE SOLUTION 51

Chapter 7
TESTIMONIALS 58

Chapter 8
IS IT SAFE? 76

Chapter 9
TECHNOLOGY—FREE 90

Chapter 1
THINGS IN YOUR HOUSE

The first questions you might ask is, "*What IS all that 'stuff' you talk about in the air inside my own house, and WHERE is it? How SERIOUS is it and, what can I do about it?*"

First off, EIGHTY percent of what's inside your house is DEAD HUMAN SKIN and the rest isn't any better. For instance, there are DUST MITES throughout your home, and a single OUNCE of dust supports FORTY-TWO THOU-SAND of them!

Airborne Dust Mites constantly eat and EXCRETE! They cause allergies; ear, eye, and nose infections; asthma attacks; fatigue; and depression. Studies show much more frightening effects of your INDOOR air.

The worst part, the reason most people do NOTHING about this problem is that THEY CAN'T SEE IT! It is, without doubt, a SILENT KILLER!

Let's start off small, like with a 1,500 square foot home which CAN generate FORTY POUNDS of dust annually. This computes (at one ounce of dust times 42,000 Dust Mites and 16 ounces to the pound, times 40 pounds of dust) to almost **27 MILLION Dust Mites!**

**This alone, even though you need
a microscope to see ONE dust mite, scares
me a little. But there's more.**

BACTERIA live in your kitchen sink, on your counter top, range, in your refrigerator, bathroom, in your heating and cooling system, on the floor, IN YOUR BED, and everywhere else in your home.

MOLD SPORES are found in your heating and air-conditioning systems, in damp clothing, carpet and drapes, wet sheet rock, in basements, under the house, in bathrooms and in kitchens.

**Mold spores can cause asthma
attacks, allergies, sinus headaches,
irritability and depression**.

I guess SO, being surrounded by this. I'd be irritable with all of this surrounding me. Again, the sad part is that it is happening so slowly that we just aren't *aware* of it, and most people—if they can't *see it, feel it or smell it,* do *nothing* about it.

⸎⸎⸎⸎⸎⸎⸎⸎

A person spends about 90% of his time INDOORS and the air INSIDE the home is four to five times MORE POLLUTED than is the OUT-SIDE air. I certainly wouldn't have believed that, but I believe the facts as they are listed.

Statistics say that you spend about one third of your living hours on earth in bed. Experts say that between two and 10 MILLION DUST MITES live in your mattress and another two or so million in your pillow! A 6-year-old pillow can get one-tenth of its weight from live Dust Mites, dead Dust Mites, and Dust Mite *feces*.

Every single time you make the bed, or fluff the pillow, an invisible and unhealthy cloud of *feces, dead skin,* and *mite body parts* circulate through the house. Ugh! A discomforting thought to say the least.

SCARE TACTICS OR FACT?

Please know that I'm not trying to frighten you by telling you these facts, it's just that few know much about INDOOR air and what it is capable of doing as far as health is concerned. And, as I researched this problem of polluted air, I learned enough for me seek out a rapid remedy.

I don't work for any company or governmental agency that deals with air pollution and I don't sell any machine or solution to combat this serious problem. I also don't understand the science behind much of what I researched, and that is why almost everyone can understand this book, because I put it in "ordinary" words.

I want you to (please) read more and not say, *"Let somebody else worry about this stuff. I don't know of anyone who has died from INDOOR AIR and I'm just not going to let it concern me."*

Well, these FACTS from different environmental agencies, from studies at *Harvard,* reports by *Peter Jennings* and a segment of *60 MINUTES* aren't kidding you. I list many of those in this chapter. And, as far as *anyone else* taking care of this FOR you—no chance. This problem exists in YOUR OWN HOME and only YOU can do something about it.

PEOPLE CAN DIE

About 64,000 people in major American Cities may be *dying annually* from lung or heart problems aggravated by breathing the gritty air pollution known as *particulates,* according to a study recently released by a national environmental group.

These microscopic particles are considered by health experts to be the **deadliest** air pollutant, yet this is the *first time* that anyone has tried to quantify the threat nationally and from city to city.

In 239 U.S. metropolitan areas, the Natural Resources Defense Council says *cardiopulmonary deaths* from *particulates* **exceed** the toll from auto accidents, as well as from AIDS and breast cancer combined. The group used *Harvard, American Cancer Society research* and *Environmental Protection Agency pollution* stats to make its estimate.

These **silent killers** aren't plastered on page one of your newspaper or over your TV except in certain sections and in documentaries—far less fun to read or watch than sports results or a cat stuck in a tree that took five fire trucks and 20 firemen to retrieve.

My heart goes out to those folks with AIDS or breast cancer but **its time** we become more aware of indoor air pollution, too.

You see, these tiny pieces of pollution spewed from diesel trucks, cars, dusty roads, power plants and an array of other sources—are small enough to lodge in lungs and aggravate respiratory and heart diseases.

"Scientists, NOT ASSOCIATED with the group's project, commended the death calculations as reasonable (even conservative) based on their own research. They used assumptions that would not give them extreme highs. In fact, they used ones that would maybe bias it a little *downward,"* said C. Arden Pope, a Brigham Young University epidemiologist.

In recent research led by the Harvard School of Public Health, Pope and other scientists concluded after tracking the health of thousands of people in six cities that particulates *shorten lives by one to three years.* The biggest risk faces the elderly and people afflicted with asthma, angina, pneumonia or other lung and heart ailments.

If this STILL seems like nothing to be concerned over, I pray that you or someone you love are not dying from one of the above maladies and would like to have an extra month to "take care of your affairs." How about an extra YEAR—or two—or THREE?

I had several close friends and relatives die in the past several years and EACH would have given almost anything to live an extra month or two. In fact, I'd have given ANYTHING to have my mother, my dad and an older brother around a few more years so I could let them know how much I loved them and how much they meant to me.

In **numbers of deaths** linked to *particulates,* the Los Angeles-Long Beach area led the nation with nearly 6,000 followed by New York, Chicago and Philadelphia. Taking the most conservative fatality-rate found in the *Harvard-American Cancer Society* study, the environmental group blamed the particulate pollution for *6.5* percent of the 980,000 annual deaths from pulmonary and heart ailments in the studied cities.

That calculates to be nearly 70,000 deaths in these cities alone that are linked DI-RECTLY to polluted air!

Pope called the death toll estimates "quite large" compared with other health threats. For example, the mortality estimated from particulates in greater Los Angeles is *four times* the number who died from auto accidents. The study comes as the Clinton administration is debating how to revise the EPA's nine-year-old health standard for particulates.

What happens, and the reason why many don't concern themselves with these particulates, is because it's not like a fire or an auto accident or a drive-by shooting where you SEE the reason for a person's death; this is an INVISIBLE enemy!

Several recent scientific studies have indicated the EPA's current standard is not stringent enough to safeguard health. The EPA faces a court order to revise it by January.

HOW DID THIS HAPPEN?

In the simplest of terms, indoor air pollution is a *predictable consequence* of a ever-growing population. But in the U.S., this problem was accelerated in the 1970's with the need to *conserve energy*. It seemed, at the time, like a good plan. This forced the construction industry to build homes and buildings that made *saving energy* a top priority. And they did.

They built houses, schools, office buildings and even factories that were insulated and *tightly sealed*. This did, in fact, save energy but it also trapped more pollutants INSIDE!

Tightly constructed buildings *can't breathe,* and very little outside air enters. This, conversely, means that very little air that is INSIDE, can get OUTSIDE. Now, is this bad? We can SEE the air outside much of the time! It seems smart to keep this out.

Well, here's the problem. As the indoor air is *recirculated*, it means the air pollutants INSIDE continue to build. All the pollutants I mentioned before are being brought into the house and *trapped*! Recent studies show the danger of this trapping effect.

GOVERNMENT INTERVENTION

I don't understand why our government doesn't step in FIRMLY and let us know that we are going to cause complications to our bodies by breathing this contaminated inside air that could result in our untimely demise. They poke their large, institutional nose into everything else.

Ironically, one of *our* agencies *created* this problem (energy conservation) when they urged us to seal our homes tighter. They *meant* well, they *meant* no harm, but it IS causing problems and scientific studies show that it is, in fact, harmful to human health and life.

Yes, even in the greatest country in the world, government officials aren't willing to stand up and take blame for a mistake, an error, an *oversight* it might be called. They made federal laws associated with motorcycle helmets, air bags, seat belts, and speeding. How about this *silent killer?*

Most local utility companies offer FREE consultation on caulking our windows and weather-stripping our doors to save on energy use. Certainly THEY are aware of the indoor air pollution problem. Yet only a small number of companies offer help in this area.

There simply MUST be a way to be energy conservative and still be healthy. I KNOW the government would like to control our lives; they are trying to gain additional control every day! I also know that we have a lot of DUMB PEOPLE in this world whose grandparents never believed in vitamins, whose parents didn't believe in vitamins, so THEY don't believe in vitamins.

These are the ones who have to be guided, who have to be TOLD, who have to be made AWARE of some of the dangers in everyday life no matter how illiterate. These are the ones who have to be SCARED into action.

I'm not calling you stupid, you understand, because those of who are reading this far into this book are the elite, the smart group, the ones who DO care and who WANT guidance if it concerns your health and the health of those you love.

And, no matter how bright YOU are, you can't know it all. The studies I've listed are by experts in their respective fields. They aren't trying to frighten you, only to inform you of their findings. I'm relaying their messages over to you. I care, and I want you to keep those you love around "a little longer" and for them to be healthier.

Over and over I say: *"People don't mind getting old (that's better than the other alternative —death), but they want to grow old PAIN FREE!"*

For instance, McDonalds and Wendy's are always advertising their specials. Are these specials healthy? Nobody cares. If we're in a hurry or on the road, we stop in for a square hamburger or a Big Mac. I do it, you do it, and I'm not condemning these places of business. The fact is, we don't eat this "stuff" every single day.

Whereas with air INDOORS we DO, in fact, **eat this stuff every day!** We breathe it while we are awake and when we are asleep. Our children breathe it and it simply MUST be made as pure as we can make it.

Yes, SOME might feel that this air pollution business about INSIDE air and those little critters crawling around our bed and pillows is nothing to worry about. What do we do? Do we *decontaminate* ourselves before we come inside so our clothing won't drag in the pollens, oils from smoke, gases, allergens and odors? Do we get dipped in some solution to get clean BEFORE we bring this outside stuff inside?

All I can tell you is what I researched. HOW you do it and IF you do it or not depends on you.

Let me tell you more of what I was able to dig up.

MORE "STUFF"

That *new furniture smell* from new carpets, drapes, upholstery and furniture is pleasing, isn't it? Well, what that REALLY is, is chemical fumes and noxious gases.

On construction sites (new homes, for instance) paint, plywood and particle board from cabinets, counter tops, and paneling emit chemical fumes, noxious gases and odors.

The furniture polish, ammonia and other cleaning products used in the homes also produce chemical vapors and harsh fumes.

Your HEATING AND COOLING SYSTEM gathers dust and moisture. Ductwork is a natural breeding ground for mold, fungi, bacteria and Dust Mites, and ductwork helps DISTRIBUTE these indoor air pollutants throughout your home and office. Again, what does all this mean? What IS the answer?

Chapter 2
A SOLUTION?

Will filters on air conditioners combat this?
NO!

The fact is that *filters* on your air-conditioning unit are for the *unit itself*. It keeps the DIRT from clogging up your air-conditioning unit; nothing more. That little filter that you buy from Wal☆Mart is for the UNIT! It is difficult for this filter to reach the air that is TRAPPED in your furniture, upholstery, drapes or carpet. This filter usually gets only the dust that is *within a few feet* of the intake, the part where the filter is placed.

These glass fiber filters regulate the AIR FLOW and some pollutants are trapped but most simply pass through into your air conditioner and heating system ductwork. That's when it meets the dust, the mold, and the moisture. THAT'S where most of the trouble begins. These filters develop "flow patterns" and the "non-flow" areas go untreated.

How about the new HIGH EFFICIENCY filters?
These aren't NEW! They do, however, trap a higher percentage of the particles. But

the effectiveness of these HEPAs is quoted by weight. Since most particles and **all** molecules are sub-micron in size, this component of bad air passes right through. Also, HEPAs are expensive, they must be changed often, and they slow down the air flow.

Aha! How about these electronic air cleaners? On these, air passes through a "charging" section where the electrically-charged plates attract the particulates. These filters are better than the ones above but they, too, must be changed or cleaned often, they cost a lot more, and when they get clogged the air flow is stopped considerably which puts a strain on your blower motor and compressor.

Let's look for a solution.

THE POSSIBILITIES

We can clean our inside air by either of three ways:

OXIDATION
DISINFECTION
PARTICULATE CONTROL

NATURE CLEANS HOUSE

You needn't be an HVAC (heating, ventilation, air conditioning) specialist to understand this, but read it carefully to see if it makes any sense to you. I hate getting "scientific" on you, but some of this is necessary to understand the BIG problem, and to find a solution.

The earth recycles her assets in many ways. One system for converting ORGANIC WASTE into fresh resources involves OZONE, the same oxygen variant that blocks UV rays in the upper atmosphere. Closer-to-home, ozone reduces dead organic "stuff" into carbon dioxide, water vapor and oxygen. Nature is remarkable!

Studies say the answer lies with *INDOOR OZONATION*! You see, air INDOORS has less ozone than air OUTDOORS, because no sun rays, no lightning bolts, waves, or waterfalls exist indoors. So, some way, we have to *capture the ozone* and move it indoors.

Absent this natural cleanser, house dust FLOATS, gathers in balls, hides in ducts, in cracks between the carpet and the wall, under sofa pillows and bothers the heck out of us. We breathe dust constantly and when we sneeze we blame it on the outside pollen. OZONE is the answer!

Ozone is a *natural disinfectant* which reduces bacteria, yeast, mold and fungi.

Natural ozone (found outside) in parts per million of .02 to .05 keeps outside air healthy. I know, what do these figures mean to you? Absolutely nothing—UNTIL you compare them with the figures for the INSIDE ozone that is manmade.

Ozone interacts with moisture (humidity) and makes small amounts of hydrogen peroxide, also a disinfectant. Thus, a DOUBLE disinfectant is about to emerge.

OZONE is nature's BEST oxidizer (other than fire). Epidemics, for example, can be stopped by BURNING the possessions and corpses of infected people. SMELL can be destroyed through burning. This is OXIDATION at its extreme.

It's like if you throw a dead rat in a fire, EVERYTHING burns; fur, flesh, entrails, bones and the rat simply go up in smoke. The rat is what they call CONVERTED via OXIDATION into carbon dioxide, water vapor, heat and a little ash.

WITHOUT the fire, the rat simply decays in a few weeks; the SMELL fades (outdoors) in a few days. If that rat (let's say a MOUSE) was poisoned INSIDE and died in your attic, the smell would drive you OUTSIDE. That's because as an oxidizer, oxygen is less powerful than the (outside) ozone.

OXIDATION—whether by fire or ozone, oxidation REDUCES many organics to their sub-components.

UNDERSTANDING OZONE

Part of what I'm going to tell you was learned from a segment of 60 Minutes because they report on any and every problem that affects us. It makes a good program, their ratings stay high, and they tell us some things in plain language that we can understand.

It is also from the encyclopedia, from Farm & Ranch magazine, from the Florida Fruit Growers Association and from a packing house I forgot the name of. These sources all talk of ozone.

Mention ozone under normal circumstances and people will think of the ozone *layer* over the earth that protects us from the sun's ultraviolet rays. But we have been able to harness ozone and make good use of it, on the earth's surface, too. For instance, ozone turns out to be a most effective *killer* of germs.

When fruit is picked from the trees, it is sometimes infected with bacteria, mold and pesticides. For decades American packers have washed food in *chlorine* but it doesn't clean away *everything* and it does leave a chemical residue. They want a better method.

Do you know how fresh the air smells after a thunderstorm? That's partly because lightning cutting through the air turns oxygen molecules (02) into *ozone*, which chemists label 03.

There is a company that manufactures ozone generators for food companies which they use to clean everything from vegetables and beef to chicken. It's simple yet effective. They use *high voltage electricity* (similar to lightning) to combine the 02 (oxygen molecules) into ozone. That ozone gas is pumped into the packing plants' water which is sprayed on the fruits.

Ozone cleans all sorts of chemicals off food, it kills *E.coli,* salmonella and bacteria, and there is a bonus because the water is now recyclable after the wash and is pumped back to the ozone generator to repeat the process. After the "vegetable water" has been filtered and treated with ozone it is beautifully clean water again, ready to be used another time—and another.

The FDA approved ozone as safe just this summer but it is not new; Japan and Europe have been using it for decades. The water supply from Los Angeles is cleaned with ozone, as is most bottled water, but for food in the United States it got little notice until the recent episodes of contamination.

Plant managers say that ozone cleaning is no more expensive than chlorine and it leaves no chemicals behind. Ozone quickly turns back into regular oxygen. As the technology spreads, it could mean a safer food supply for a worried public. This brings us back to our home and our INDOOR air that is, without a doubt, polluted.

OUTSIDE AIR IS SAFER

I *squinch* up my face on this one; it doesn't seem likely. I've flown over major cities where you had to actually *cut* through layers of "stuff" that was hovering over tall buildings. There is NO WAY the air inside my house is messier than this!

I can SEE this outside smoke—different colors even—hanging in clouds. And I can SMELL it, too. Maybe they are talking about air in the desert, or Yosemite, or the islands in the South Pacific, or in the jungles but in the U.S., I don't believe it. Explain it to me!

You're right—and wrong! Certainly in areas where there are factories, or big cities with hundreds of thousands of cars spewing exhaust fumes, or on subways or busses where smokers are breathing all over you it is unhealthy. And I am talking about air beyond these particular areas, but for the first time in history it may be safer to be out *in the wilderness* than to be in our own home. Why? Because Americans spend *90% of their time* indoors breathing a noxious soup of contaminates.

In a typical home or office dust and dirt enter and are *trapped* in the mat of our carpet. Doctors advise us that dust is the last great medium of human infection. Germs have no means of locomotion except to attach themselves to particles of dust.

Experts warn that various fumes of cleaning products can cause *learning disabilities.* There are actual cases of people who have been *poisoned* by their own homes. It is estimated that a homemaker is only 30% efficient in cleaning because of dust stirring up and moving from room to room. A chair contains residue from every person that has ever sat on it. Who was there before you?

The ceiling—styrene, fiberglass and wood, all are porous material and convenient places for accumulation of disease causing pollution. If we

Chapter 3
SICK BUILDING SYNDROME

The term means that a building has faulty air conditioning or ducts or fiberglass or even something 'mysterious' which makes the building unsafe. In attempting to write this book, I HAD to find out more. If you're interested, read about it.

⟡⟡⟡⟡⟡ ⟡⟡⟡⟡⟡

The condition known as *sick building syndrome* became popularized in the early 1980's, when the oil embargo started to make building owners more conscious of the need to save energy.

A big building has to have air flowing just like a fish tank has to have oxygenated water, and if you dump too many chemicals on or too much food in the tank it is going to sour and the fish will begin floating to the top. With a *sick building* that is exactly what is happening.

Architects began to design buildings with windows that didn't open, or sometimes even *windowless* buildings. This lack of ventilation has allowed fungus to flourish and make some buildings "sick," according to Texas Tech researchers headed by microbiologist David Straus.

"At first, researchers thought carpet cleaner or dusting chemicals were to blame, but for years other scientists suspected that fungus might be the culprit."

One of the problems has been getting owners of buildings to allow researchers to test the air for fungus. Many building owners are fearful of lawsuits.

"This is the first study to achieve statistical significance by actually testing dozens of buildings," said Straus. Straus and his research team were able to gain access to the school buildings because of a relationship with a Dallas company that maintains air quality for schools in Texas.

Researchers believe that through control of the electrical charges in the air we breathe, our moods, energy and health can be markedly improved.

Texas Tech researchers announced recently that they have found a significant cause of *sick building syndrome*, blamed for causing office workers and school children to develop hay fever-like symptoms over the past decade.

The study, to be published in the September 1999 edition of the *British Journal of Occupational and Environmental Medicine,* looked at 48 school buildings and found that two types of fungus were common to them all—*penicillium* and *stachybotrys.*

"Buildings in which *penicillium* has become dominant in the air will cause people to experience allergic reactions," he said. "*Stachybotrys* has toxins that cause toxic reactions."

Straus said the Texas Tech study should help identify whether buildings where people complain of headaches, watery eyes and respiratory problems actually *have* sick building syndrome and help to determine when the problem has been corrected.

"Once the fungi is eliminated from the air by increasing ventilation and eliminating standing water, the symptoms stop."

But researchers say the news is not all good. *Stachybotrys,* is a deadly fungus believed to be responsible for the deaths of six children in Cleveland in 1989. Doctors never conclusively proved *stachybotrys* was to blame, but many think that the fungus caused the children to have a toxic reaction so severe that it caused their capillaries (tiny blood vessels) throughout the body to burst. They are thought to have choked to death on their own blood.

Straus said that even though his team of researchers never detected enough of the fungus in the school buildings they studied to pose a mortal threat, they were concerned when they found that stachybotrys was involved.

"At first we thought penicillium might be the only fungus involved, but that wouldn't explain some of the neurological symptoms some people reported, like dizziness and double vision."

"We found that those symptoms are toxic reactions to stachybotrys, which is an entirely different kind of beast. It's much more dangerous and thrives in damp places."

World Health Organization spokesman Dan Epstein said other studies are focusing on whether sick building syndrome might be caused by carpet glue or binding chemical used to install floors. He said that the organization would probably review the Tech study when it is published.

Since air is so vital, shouldn't it be clean? According to the EPA, there are three solutions:

✔ **Eliminate all sources of pollution.**
This is not entirely practical since you and your family still have to live or work there.

✔ **Increase ventilation.**

But what if the air you bring *in* is not fresh? If you live near a city or factory, it might not be. And did you know that on the *best ventilation systems* only ⅓ of the air is exchanged? Moreover, this becomes costly during the heating or cooling seasons.

✔ Filter and reuse the air.

Great idea, how do you do this? But this method can be truly ineffective since only 10% of the air in a home ever gets circulated through a filter. Literally you would need dozens of filters in your home to accomplish much.

So, what IS the solution? We're aware that the air is polluted and we want it to be clean? Do we get sprayed like fruit and vegetables with ozoneated water? Let's look at the way *nature* cleans the air.

The sun puts off electric charges, changing some particulates in the air to a negative charge. These negative charges are attracted to the existing positive charges and when these particles join they become heavy and cannot stay airborne. The suns rays also create *low-level ozone.*

As nature's most potent oxidizing agent, *ozone*, completes nature's process to reducing contaminates to harmless natural substances,

we've found a way to put nature into our homes.
Let me share with you THE solution to all of this.

Chapter 4
UNDERSTANDING CLEAN AIR

I've already complimented those of you who have gotten this far into this book. Yet, even though you're bright, it doesn't necessarily mean that this particular side of your brain understands scientific jargon or that you even care to read about it.

Now this is basic stuff, but you can pass over it if you choose. I, as a person whose mind doesn't think in these areas (or care) put it in for those of you who do care.

To me, it's like an air conditioner; I could care less that it has refrigerant, a filter, compressor, condenser or whatever—I don't CARE how it works, I just want to touch a button and have it COOL me! But, here goes.

❧❧❧❧❧ ❧❧❧❧❧

Natural fresh air contains three ingredients normally absent from **INDOOR** air:

1. An electrical charge (ionization).
2. Small quantities of ozone (O^3).
3. Adequate air circulation.

Equipment using these processes has achieved 80% reductions in mold, mildew and bacteria and helps control particles. In addition, dust mites do not thrive where ozone is present. Most people would agree with these statements, except for the word "ozone."

WHAT IS OZONE?

The misunderstanding about ozone is based on its confusion with pollution. Because there are many different pollutants (some 3,600 in cigarette smoke alone), it is difficult and expensive to measure each one. It is far easier to measure the ozone, nature's response to the pollution. Therefore, it has become commonplace for weathermen to announce the degree of pollution in terms of ozone.

Ozone is easy to monitor, but it is merely *an index* to the real pollution. An appropriate analogy would be the relationship of the white cell count in blood to infection. The white cell count is determined by the amount of infection present, but it is there to *fight* the infection. It's the same with ozone. With high pollution levels, more ozone is formed, but that ozone is working to break down the pollutants.

The next time someone expresses concern about the safety of ozone ask the, *"Would you want to breathe a gas that in certain concentrations causes cramps, nausea, dizziness, hypothermia, ambylopia, respiratory difficulties. bradycardia, fainting spells and convulsions capable of leading to death?"*

When they reply, "No," tell them that these symptoms result from breathing oxygen (O^2) in concentrations. Anything (including oxygen and ozone) can be undesirable at high levels. One can drown in too much water. The reaction people have to ozone would lead people to say that because people have drowned in water, water is dangerous and shouldn't be allowed indoors.

However, we do have water indoors because we have a faucet which *controls* the amount we use. Likewise, *air purifiers* which **control the ozone level** are equally safe. They reproduce only the *necessary* small quantities of ozone present in natural fresh air.

Ozone is found throughout nature. The ozone layer in the upper atmosphere is created by the interaction of sunlight (UV rays) with oxygen (O_2), and protects us from harmful ultraviolet radiation.

Ozone is also created in the *lower* atmosphere. Lightning in thunderstorms split oxygen molecules leading to higher than usual concentrations of ozone. That *fresh, clean smell* after a rainstorm is often due to ozone. Now follow this next part; it's simple, and you needn't be a chemist or weatherman to understand it.

Everyday sunlight splits some of the O_2 molecules into single oxygen molecules, which then attach themselves to other O_2 molecules, creating ozone (O_3). This is an *unstable bond* and when the O_3 molecules contact pollutants, the single oxygen molecule attaches itself to them, thus oxidizing them.

In the case of chemicals, it begins to break down the molecular bond of that molecule, and if there is enough ozone present, it will eventually destroy that molecule's bond completely, thereby neutralizing it. All organic chemicals are broken down eventually into water vapor, carbon dioxide, oxygen and a few other basic elements.

Automobile exhaust and industrial plant emissions are the two principal sources of *smog*. A photochemical reaction takes place when these emissions (sunlight, moisture and heat) combine in the right set of circumstances.

A single oxygen atom is removed which then combines with atmospheric oxygen, to form ozone.

The ozone is reported as the "smog level." But what about the other chemicals? We don't hear about the combination of various harmful com- pounds such as *nitrogen dioxide, nitric acid, nitrous oxide, sulfur dioxide, sulfuric acid, carbonic acid* and *carbon monoxide*. These are the *real* pollutants.

Naturally-occurring ozone is colorless, not the grayish-brown color associated with smog! Ozone is easy to monitor, but it is merely an index to the real pollution. When there is a high level of pollution, more ozone is formed, but that ozone is working to break down the chemicals.

Chapter 5
IONS AND IONIZATION

One sweltering day in Philadelphia this summer a man sat before a small metal box resting atop a hospital file cabinet. It was plugged into an ordinary wall socket. A doctor flipped a switch. Inside the box a small fan whirred; the box hummed distantly like a high-tension wire, and gave off a faint, sweetish odor. Soon the man felt alert and magically refreshed, as though he'd been taking deep gulps of sparkling October air.

The doctor turned the machine off, and switched on another that looked just like it. The air grew quickly stale. The man s head felt stuffy. His eyes smarted. His head began to ache. He felt vaguely depressed and tired.

With this simple experiment, the scientist, *Dr. Igho H. Kornblueh*, of the American Institute of Medical Climatology, demonstrated the effect that *atmospheric ions* can have on human beings. The first machine generated negative ions; the second, positive ions.

The air around us is filled with these electrically charged particles. They are generated in invisible billions by cosmic rays, radioactive elements in the soil, ultraviolet radiation, storms, waterfalls, winds, and the friction of blowing sand or dust.

Every time we draw a breath these ions enter the lungs. They appear to have a lot to do with such varied things as our moods, why cattle grow skittish before a storm, why rheumatic joints tingle when the barometer falls, and how ants know in advance that it's going to rain in time to block their tunnels.

POSITIVE EFFECT OF NEGATIVE IONS

Falling barometric pressure and hot, dry, seasonal winds, such as Alpine *foehn* (warm dry wind blowing down into the valleys of a mountain, especially the Alps) and the Rocky Mountain *chinook (on the eastern slope of the Rockies*, a warm, dry wind coming from the north or west) and the Pacific Coast Santa Ana winds for example, pack the air with an excess of positive ions.

Not everyone is affected; healthy young people swiftly adapt to the change. But countless others are distressed. The *aged* come down with respiratory complaints, aching joints; asthma sufferers wheeze and gasp; children grow cranky and perverse; crime and suicide rates climb.

On the other hand, a preponderance of

negative ions spices the air with exhilarating freshness. We feel on top of the world. *Dr. C. W. Hansell*, research fellow at RCA Laboratories and an international authority on ionization, illustrates the effect with a story about his ten-year-old daughter.

"We were outside, watching the approach of a thunderstorm. I knew that clouds of negative ions were filling the air. Suddenly my daughter began to dance across the grass, a radiant look on her face. She leaped up on a low boulder, threw her arms wide to the dark sky, and cried, 'Oh, I feel wonderful!'" Negative ions *cure* nothing that we know of, at most they afford relief only so long as one inhales them. Many doctors doubt their therapeutic effects. But there is a growing army of people who swear by them.

TOTAL RELIEF

At the University of Pennsylvania's Graduate Hospital and at Northeastern and Frankford hospitals in Philadelphia, Dr. Kornblueh and his associates have administered negative-ion treatments to hundreds of patients suffering from hay fever or bronchial asthma.

Of the total, 63 percent have experienced

partial to total relief. "They come in sneezing, eyes watering, noses itching, worn out from lack of sleep, so miserable they can hardly walk." One doctor told me that 15-minutes in front of the negative-ion machine and they feel so much better they didn't want to leave.

It was RCA's Dr. Hansell who, in 1932, stumbled upon the behavioral effects of artificially generated ions. He noticed a startling swing in the moods of a fellow RCA scientist who worked beside an electrostatic generator.

Some days the scientist finished work alert and in bubbling good spirits. On other days he was rude, ill-tempered and depressed. Dr. Hansell investigated and found that when the generator produced *negative* ions he was fine, but morose when the machine was producing *positive* ions. A few months later, reports of ionization research in Europe confirmed the strange experience.

A few years ago atmospheric ions became suddenly important to *military researchers* in environmental medicine. How would they affect men locked in submarines? In space ships? What *were* the possibilities of ion therapy? Research programs multiplied with fantastic results.

AN EFFECTIVE PAINKILLER

Dr. Kornblueh studied brain-wave patterns and found evidence that negative ions *tranquilized* persons in severe pain. In one dramatic test he held a negative ionizer to the nose and mouth of a factory worker who had been rushed to Northeastern Hospital with second-degree burns on his back and legs.

In minutes the pain was gone. Morphine, customarily administered in such cases, was never necessary.

Today *all* burn cases at Northeastern Hospital are immediately put in a windowless, *ion-conditioned* room. In ten minutes, usually, the pain is gone. Patients are left in the room for 30 minutes. The treatment is repeated three times every 24 hours. In 85 percent of the cases no pain-deadening narcotics are needed.

Northeastern's Dr. Robert McGowan says, "negative ions make burns dry out faster, heal faster and with less scarring. They also reduce the need for skin-grafting. They make the patient more optimistic as well as causing them to sleep better."

Encouraged by this success in burn therapy, Dr. Kornblueh, Dr. J. R. Minehart, Northeastern's chief, surgeon, and his associate Dr. T. A. David, boldly tried negative ions in relief of deep, post-operative pain.

During an eight-month test period they exposed 138 patients to negative ions on the first and second days after surgery. Dr. Kornblueh has just announced the results at a London congress of bioclimatologists. In 79 cases—*57 percent of the total*—negative ions eliminated or drastically reduced pain.

"At first," says Dr. Minehart, "I thought it was voodoo. Now I'm convinced that it's real and revolutionary." Experiments by Dr. Albert F. Krueger and Dr. Richard Smith at the University of California have shown how ionization affects those sensitive to airborne allergens.

Our bronchial tubes and trachea (windpipe) are lined with tiny filaments called cilia. The cilia normally maintain a whip-like motion of about 900 beats a minute. Together with mucus, they keep our air passage free of dust and pollen. Krueger and Smith exposed tracheal tissue to negative ions, found that the ciliary beat was speeded up to 1,200 a minute and that mucus flow was increased.

Doses of *positive* ions produced the *opposite* effect, ciliary beat slowed to 600 a minute or less; the flow of mucus dropped.

COUNTERACTING CANCER

In experiments that may prove important in cancer research, Drs. Krueger and Smith also discovered that *cigarette smoke* slows down the cilia and impairs their ability to clear foreign, and possibly carcinogenic (cancer-inducing), substances from the lungs.

Positive ions, administered along with the cigarette smoke, lowered the ciliary beat as before, but from three to ten times *faster* than in normal air. **Negative ions**, however, *counteracted* the effects of the smoke, observed Dr. Krueger. "The agent in cigarette smoke that slows down the ciliary beat is not known."

Whatever it may be, its action is effectively neutralized by *negative ions,* which raise the ciliary beat as well as in a heavy atmosphere of cigarette smoke as they do in fresh air.

MOOD ALTERATION

How do ions trip off our moods?
Most authorities agree that ions act on our capacity to absorb and utilize oxygen. Negative ions in the bloodstream accelerate the delivery of oxygen to our cells and tissues, fre-

quently giving us the same euphoric jolt that we get from a few whiffs of straight oxygen.

Positive ions *slow down* the delivery of oxygen, producing symptoms markedly like those in anoxia, or oxygen starvation. Researchers also believe that negative ions may stimulate the *reticulo-endothelial* system (a group of defense cells in our bodies which marshal our resistance to disease).

Dr. Krueger predicts that we shall someday regulate the ion level indoors much as we now regulate temperature and humidity.

Ironically, today's air-conditioned buildings, trains, and planes frequently become super-charged with harmful *positive ions* because the metal blowers, filters and ducts of air-conditioning systems strip the air of negative ions before it reaches its destination. This explains why so many people in air-conditioned spots feel depressed and have an urge to throw open a window.

Air conditioner manufacturers are designing new systems that increase negative ionization. The American Broadcasting Co. will equip its new 30-story New York City headquarters with ion control. Two national concerns, Philco and Emerson Electric, already have ion-control air-conditioning systems on the market. RCA, Westinghouse,

General Electric and Carrier Corp. have similar products under study or development.

We still have much to learn about atmospheric ions. But researchers believe that these magic bits of electricity, under artificial control, will soon be helping millions to healthier, happier, more productive lives. And through control of the electrical charges in the air, our moods, energy and health can be markedly improved.

Chapter 6
THE SOLUTION

My next research brought me to a company in Tennessee that makes what many believe to be the very BEST air purification systems in America today—Alpine Industries.

This firm offers air purification systems that recreate nature's own air purifying process by using ions to *sweep* contaminants from the air, and creating ozone molecules to oxidize and eliminate pollution.

Their systems make indoor air mountain fresh; hence the name Alpine. Nothing is as fresh or makes us feel better than to take a deep breath of fresh clean air. Alpine is the recognized leader and far and away the largest manufacturer in the U.S. air purification industry.

AN INDUSTRY LEADER

First, let me explain that I do not SELL Alpine filters, purifying units or any machines. I sell books—NOTHING ELSE. I know of this company simply because I researched them and found them on the Internet. I don't know any of their officers, I never talked to them on the telephone, had dinner with them nor do I know the church they belong to.

I have some of their literature, their newsletter and one of their sales brochure; I got it from the distributor who sold me my X-15 unit. I used this product and IMMEDIATELY I could breathe easier. I did, in fact, feel as if I were outside breathing the clean air we all feel after a recent thunderstorm when I walked INSIDE my home.

You remember my telling you about an air conditioner; I don't truly understand how it works and don't CARE. I just want to turn it on and have it cool ME. Well, it's the same with an air purifier. I don't build them, I just own one that works!

But if I got a book written in REGULAR words that I could understand, I might want to know a little bit more. So I'm going to now, share with you the TECHNICAL EXPLANATION of the Alpine model I have—the XL-15.

WHAT EXACTLY IS IT?

It is the personal computer, the telephone, the VCR, the microwave. It is a revolutionary, simple, *affordable* solution to a complex, widespread problem.

In hindsight, it is obvious: like using a wheel to transport a load. Great ideas are like that. They often make you say, "Why didn't I think of that?"

The XL-15 (also called *Living Air*) has a history that reads like "Who's Who" in the Greatest Innovations of the World.

The first car was a nuisance. So was the first telephone. The first televisions were an appliance only the rich could afford. Computers were once just for nerds and accountants. The VCR was expensive and complex. Even though most people still can't program them, there is one in almost every American home today.

These products all have two things in common; they were daring, "science fiction" cutting-edge, and they *revolutionized our lives*. They forever changed how we travel, how we communicate, how we work, and how we are entertained.

NOBODY thought they needed any of these things. People weren't sitting around before the car came along saying, "*I'm sick to death of riding a horse or sitting in this stupid buggy. What I really need is a car!*" A lot of good that would have done them anyway. There were no roads and no gasoline stations.

When the inventor of Alpine *Living Air* systems emerged from his basement with that little wooden box with a fan in it under his arm saying that it would purify the air in your home, nobody even cared. Let me share *that* story with you.

THE START OF INDOOR PURIFICATION

I got the following information from a copy of Money Makers Magazine dated December 1996. This is what I discovered.

Alpine Founder, Bill Converse, studied Electrical Engineering at University of Nebraska. In 1984 he was retained to write an engineering study for another company but their product didn't work. Bill saw how to fix the problem and offered to help but they said no. So he built it himself.

"I knew the problems associated with filtration and became intrigued with the idea of using electrical technologies to actually PURIFY the air the same way as it's done in nature. There are no filters outside and there are plenty of pollutants."

The first units were made in Converse's home by Bill and his daughter Karen. His new "oxygen" machine worked. The timing was right.

Converse was so far ahead of his time that almost no one knew what he was talking about. He had invented a solution for a problem the average person didn't even know existed. But as things do, when timing and genius and opportunity meet on destiny's bridge, the winds of change began to blow.

Chronic fatigue and sick-building syndrome were added to the dictionary. Indoor air quality and soaring respiratory ailments became frequent subjects of discussion in newspapers and on government panels. As the experts began to identify the problem and search for a solution, the term "Living Air" was coined and its obscure inventor became an international authority.

His little gadget became the topic for talk show discussions. Experts took the box apart piece by piece, argued over its merits, taunted its claims and in the pattern of all significant innovations, they did their best to discredit the machine and its maker.

The "Thunderstorm in a Box," as someone labeled it, was about as flashy as a Model T and as user-friendly as a rotary phone, but it worked! It worked so well that people could smell the difference. They told friends who told friends and now more than 2.5 million units have been sold.

So-called experts and cynics warned that further testing was essential to prove that the new technology is "safe for humans," but in reality, Living Air used nothing new to produce its startling results. "In fact," says the inventor, "we used technology as old as the earth itself to cleanse and purify the air in your home naturally."

Every time the sun comes up, every time the lightning strikes across the sky, it cleanses the air outside. We copied that process, 'harnessed it,' so to speak, and brought it inside."

Inc. magazine recently reported Alpine to be the 84th fastest growing, privately-held company in America. In 1997, sales exceeded $100 million. And although the XL-15 looks no more imposing than a small stereo speaker, it's causing quite a stir. So, you might want to get a little tea and head for the harbor; it looks like a revolution has begun.

Had I found other manufacturers of similarly effective air purifiers, I certainly would have mentioned them, too. But, I didn't.

I did, however, pick up *rumors* of other brands that might be just as good, but I could only find sketchy information that was unconvincing on blurred photocopies. I decided that Alpine was pretty much the only serious manufacturer in this emerging new industry.

Next I looked for testimonials from people who are using Alpine's Living Air systems and I recorded some here for you to look over and

identify with. This next chapter lists but some of
the testimonials.

Chapter 7
TESTIMONIALS

I just *love* testimonials. They are from people with problems and their problems are solved. They are (usually) written in words we can all understand and when another "regular human being" tells what has happened to him because of some medication or some machine, we want to know about it. We want to have it work on us. I edited the following only slightly, taking special care not to change the content.

SALON SHOP ODORS ELIMINATED

Thank goodness I went over this a time or two before this book went to press. Actually, one of my editors caught it. I had for a beginning title "Salon Shop OWNER Eliminated." But, thankfully, that wasn't the case.

A hair salon has many chemicals and odors in the air at all times. Between the hair color, bleaches, perm solutions, hair sprays, artificial nail solvents, and acrylic solutions combined it can make for an unpleasant odor as well as a serious environmental problem.

The letter:"I had an air system in my house

and it cleaned the air and made my entire home smell fresh so I thought I'd try it for my shop. The air purifiers have eliminated not only the odors, but have cleaned up the air so well that even our complexions are better! It's true! All of the staff has noticed cleaner, less oily complexions and best of all—fewer illnesses."

M.P.
Cosmetologist/Salon Manager

SCHOOLS USE THEM

"We have staff and students with asthma, and they can feel the difference in their breathing when they enter our facilities. When we had the health alert last month, the air purifiers were a life saver. Parent's noticed the change immediately as did the students and staff.

Children who were coughing when they were outside and in their cars, stopped the instant they came into our building. I know that anyone with any health problems will truly benefit from air purifiers."

J.S.
Greenwood Christian Preschool
Houston, TX

ASTHMATICS APPRECIATE CLEANER AIR

"I have severe asthma and have been using a *pulmo-aide* up to four times a day for several years. Since purchasing the Alpine system, I am finding myself not needing to use my *pulmo-aide*. I have prayed for better health for a long time and I truly believe that Alpine is an answer to my prayers.

Our entire home smells fresh and clean and I now sleep better than I have in years. The only change I made was by using the air purifier."

L.B.
Savannah, GA

CLEANS AND FRESHENS A PET HOSPITAL

"I've been a veterinarian for twenty-six years. Your Alpine system took my "clinic smell" completely out and replaced it with healthier, oxygenated/ionized, revitalized air. My children noticed it first. They were so familiar with that animal clinic odor that they 'could smell' me coming. No more!

My wife has allergies that numbed her nose to the air in my animal hospital and she noticed a change in the smell and actual 'feel' of the air a short time after I had the system installed. The clinic smells so great that I bought another unit for my kennel area.

Again, success? It has effectively controlled the odors there as well, and the air is cleaner, healthier and smells better. It has brought a cleanliness to my clinic that even the most expensive scrubs and chemicals combined with strenuous scoring could not bring. An almost odorless animal clinic is miraculous.

One of my employees, who was bothered with allergies, felt better immediately and bought the XL-15 cleaner (the model I have) for her own home."

L.C.
Centerville Animal Hospital
Lithonia, GA

SMELLY BASEMENT

"We bought a house which had some weird odors coming up from our basement. There was a musty smell as well as the real culprit, a sewage odor. We had three different plumbers come out to resolve the problem by using solutions which ranged from digging up our back yard to 'not a clue.' Finally, we had heard of this negative ion generator machine which could 'clean up' the air and so we were lucky to have found you and tried one.

"We first tried the XL-15 for about 10 days and it helped, but the total odor problem was still lingering. Then we added the Eagle model to our basement. After several days, the penetrating ions *totally cleared* up the remaining odor.

"Yesterday, we got our own unit, placed it in the basement and now the entire house is WON-DERFUL! I guess it took a strong hit of the power of two machines to really get all over the house. Our house is nearly 3,500 square feet if you include the basement."

B.W.
ST. Louis, MO

SINUS PAIN GONE

"In the past ten years I have had two sinus surgeries. Since the operation (that did *not* help) I've been taking ten *Contact* a day for ten years to avoid sinus infection. We have made two runs to

Mexico to get *Ceclor* and *Keflex* to fight sinus infection, and also to get blood pressure medication.

"In less than two months (after I bought the air purifier) I have not taken even ONE *Contact* or ANY OTHER sinus medication. That totals to NOT taking approximately 480 'other pills' during that time.

"My blood pressure has come down because I am not taking sinus medication, and I will reduce the blood pressure medication carefully. I have noticed it is easier to urinate, and there is no pain *now!*

"I take the smaller of the two units with me when I have to stay out of town to use in the motel room. I showed it to a Super 8 Motel manager and he said '*Oh yes, our motels use them when a room smells bad.*'

"I had to take a smoking room at a motel one night because there was no other available. It almost "knocked me out." I turned on a small unit I had with me and went to get a sandwich. When I returned, you couldn't smell the smoke!"

L.P.
White Bear Lake, MN

DOCTOR SAYS IT'S GOOD

"I have always known the importance of clean air, clean water and good food and its effects on the human body. I became particularly interested in the technology that Alpine uses to accomplish air purification when you shared it with me. At first, even with my science background, it seemed too good to be true and I have to admit I was a bit skeptical. I thank you for allowing our clinic to try it for a few days, that is exactly what we needed to be convinced of its value.

"I have since shared the value of indoor air purification with many people and the stories I'm having are too numerous to account here in this letter. The need for this product is truly overwhelming."

Dr. M.V.M
Woodbury, MN

GET RID OF THAT SMOKING DOG

We can put a man on the moon but we cannot get rid of the odor on one of our dogs. I've been told that "the only way to get rid of the dog

ODOR, is to get rid of the DOG."

"For about three years, my wife and I investigated a variety of so-called *air purifiers* ranging from $30 up. We went for several $70 models which are now all in our closet.

"I have been a devout pipe smoker for many years and although the aroma is pleasing to *me*, others complained about it. My wife and I also have two fairly large house dogs—one of which has always been plagued with a rather *pungent* odor that emanates from her no matter what is done to correct it. As a result, our 2,000 square foot home always smelled like a dirty dog smoking a pipe!

"One day my wife came home with the XL-15 air purifier that was loaned to her to try. My first words were 'That little thing is going to do the whole house? Yeah, sure.' Well, much to the amazement of both of us, our house was *totally odorless* within a couple of hours! Not long after my wife was able to discontinue her allergy medication for the first time in many years, we could no longer see dust floating in the air, the air seemed 'lighter' and easier to breathe, and a multitude of other benefits were noticed."

C.B.
Savannah, GA

NO MORE HEADACHES

"I am a photographer, and I bought the XL-15 for my dark room to help eliminate the chemical odors, especially Glacial Acetic Acid. In the 25 years I have worked with this chemical, I have always gotten a headache if I had been in contact with it for more than two hours.

"I have overhead hoods and suction fans, but it never helped. Thanks to your 'Living Air' unit, I have yet to have a headache and, now, will work the darkroom for four to six hours. In addition to this obvious benefit, the room has lost the *dark-room odors.* I will recommend it to anyone."

B.H., Owner
Impact

HAIR AND NAIL SALON

"In our hair and nail salon we have a lot of different smells including perms and nail products. On busy days sometimes the smells can *knock your socks off!* You were nice enough to let us try your system for a few days. What a difference! It is clean and fresh smelling all day, we have never had this result from anything else we have ever tried."

D.M.F.
Manicurist/Salon Owner

THE RITZ CARLTON

"We were on the verge of installing a major system in our grill to accommodate the cigar smoking, but your system has proven very effective for this purpose. Its compact size and quiet operation is exactly what we needed."

M.K., Director of Operations
The Ritz-Carlton
Phoenix, AZ

COUGHING AND ASTHMA GONE

"In December I purchased an XL-15 system. Having only read literature, I took a chance that this product would do what the brochure states that is; clean the air of mildew. Not only did my house smell better, but I feel it has done more.

"My daughter is almost five years old and since birth she has coughed every night. The cough was a deep sort of cough that constantly sounded as if she had pneumonia or a deep chest cold.

"Within a few days after using the XL-15, she stopped coughing. Skeptical, we waited a few more nights but the cough was never heard. It's been almost two months now and only *once* has she coughed (she indeed had a cold). Since birth we have had her into the doctor for this cough numerous times but found nothing.

"My wife has Asthma. Her allergies sometimes make it hard for her to breathe. On numerous occasions I have taken her to the emergency room because of it. Since your unit has been in, she has not used her atomizer with the frequency she had to use it before.

"Our entire family now wakes up in the morning with clear breathing. Especially in this colder weather when stuffy noses due to the drier air are prevalent."

R.R.J.

FOOTBALL LOCKER ROOM

"I am the football equipment manager at the University of North Carolina and in charge of general maintenance of our locker room. We purchased several of your Living Air units last summer because we have had problems with various odors throughout the year and have unsuccessfully tried many products to resolve them.

"We have noticed a major improvement in the locker room smell and atmosphere. The number of colds and general illnesses on our football team seems to have decreased also. We have been especially pleased with the fact that these units *produce fresh clean smelling air* without creating their own strong odor."

D.M., Manager
University of North Carolina Football Equipment

STOPPED ALL MEDICATION

"Our air purifiers have helped me with my health and has stopped a monthly expenditure of $125 on prescription drugs I have been taking since 1991.

"My allergies and sinus problems have caused me to lose my sense of smell. You can't imagine how this feels until you have experienced not being able to smell almost anything.

"After putting your small unit in our bedroom and an XL-15 in the main part of our home, I started feeling better the following night. Seven days later I stopped all medication. Within two weeks I was able to smell everything, including the roses in our back yard. What a wonderful feeling.

"My doctor cannot *believe* what the units are doing for me. He asked for some information about the units and I have forwarded it to him."

M.B.
Bernard Associates
Los Gatos, CA

AUTO EXHAUST

"Our drive-in banks have been plagued with bad odors caused by the automobiles of customers. The complaints of the walk-in customers convinced us that we needed to do *something*.

"The introduction of air purification into our branch banks have had a remarkable effect on the air quality and our employees have been pleased with the change. We recommend this technology highly."

D.L.J.
Senior Executive VP
Knoxville, IA

A LONG STORY BUT A GOOD ONE

"In May of 1989, while working at my job on Robins Air Force Base, my lungs became so weak that I could not breathe. I found myself asking for help and an ambulance was called. At that moment I felt sure I was going to die.

"I was rushed to the hospital and the doctors worked on me for a solid *hour* before I was able to begin breathing on my own. The doctor told me that it was very likely that I would have to remain on oxygen for the *remainder of my life* and keep an oxygen tank with me at all times.

"'I had been a smoker for the past 35 years and was diagnosed as having emphysema. The treatment involved breathing therapy and required that I use a breathing machine at home. I did not want to use oxygen for any length of time because

I knew that it could be as addictive as cigarettes.

"For approximately three years I was on breathing treatments, various medications and carried an inhaler with me at all times. With all the medications and treatments I continued to have severe breathing problems. I could no longer cough up the phlegm that coated my lungs, and the medication had ceased to help.

"I no longer slept through the night, and my coughing was so severe there were times I felt I should call 911 for assistance. My neck became extremely painful from the nicotine having partially stopped up the main arteries that carry the blood to my brain. I was put on medication to relieve the neck hurt. I realized I had reached a point where the medication and treatment was no longer effective.

"In September of 1992 a good friend of mine came to my home and introduced me to an air purifier made by Alpine Industries. He told me that purifying the air in our home should help me to breathe easier. For the first time since May of 1989, I slept for eight hours straight. I knew then that I had found a key to my health problems.

"My sinuses began to run and the phlegm began to break up. These symptoms persisted and I realized that the many toxins in my body were being eliminated. This process took approximately a year.

"In January of 1994 I stopped using the breathing machine completely and in December of the same year, my lung specialist upgraded my diagnosis of emphysema to asthma. My last test showed that my breathing was at 98%.

"I am thoroughly convinced that my improvement over the last two and a half years is directly due to the Living Air purifier. "

E.T.
Warner Robins, GA

FOR ALLERGIES

"Since December 1991, I have used air purifiers with many of our patients who suffer from severe upper respiratory allergies.

"Most suffer from house dust, pollen, dander, mold, mildew and many chemical compounds. In every case the patients have responded with almost no new attacks, while indoors.

"These machines are excellent for removing the various allergens from the indoor environment, thereby alleviating allergic reactions. I should also mention that those with asthma do well on low settings.

"The most gratifying experience was when I loaned an air purifier to a patient referred by Dr. Foster Montalbano, M.D. This patient had severe allergies and she was allowed to use the machine for a few days. She later bought the machine and responded in a letter that said, *'I LOVE IT! I LOVE IT! I LOVE IT! I will never give it up, thank you for this wonderful purifier'.*"

J.E.S., Ph.D.
Immunologist
Annandale, VA

CAT URINE SMELL ELIMINATED

A very strong tears-in-the-eyes cat urine order was present in the house during certain atmospheric conditions. Numerous attempts to eliminate the problem by other methods failed. Use of industrial strength odor neutralizing chemicals; replacement of drywall sections; sealing and painting of walls/trim with industrial strength odor/stain sealer and paint; cleaning and sealing of floors; replacement of carpet tack strips and elimination of the animal from the premises.

"After four days of localized placement of the XL-15 in known problem spots, and centralized treatment (by floor levels) in this 2,000 square foot split-level house, the odor was gone.

"The second test was to determine if the odor would return after the removal of the machine. I am happy to report that after two weeks the odor did *not* return.

"The third and final test was to expose the treated house to a prospect who had placed a contingency on buying the property only if the odor was eliminated. We sold the property to this prospect.

"The XL-15 performed its advertised purpose in what I consider to be a worst case situation. I highly recommend it to anyone who wants to breathe fresh air.

R.M., Realtor, Ph.D.
Camp Hill, PA

Chapter 8
IS IT SAFE?

What IS this little "THUNDERSTORM IN A BOX" machine that seems to work wonders on cleansing the indoor air that is steadily becoming more problematical and unhealthy?

It isn't large; I measured mine. It's 10 inches tall, 8 inches wide, 12 inches deep and weighs a mere 16 pounds.

It is used to purify the air in homes up to 3,000 square feet, moldy basements, dusty attics, closets, stale vacation homes, water damaged properties, working or sleeping areas, sick buildings (offices), nursing homes, hospices, hotel and motel rooms.

It takes out the odors from smoking areas, beauty salons, barber shops, kitchens, food service areas, cafeterias, veterinary clinics, kennels, daycare centers, community rooms, meeting rooms and skunk odors.

It eliminates the odors in garbage and trash areas, businesses that generate various odors, chemicals, airborne particulates, auto dealerships, locker rooms, fish markets, meat storage lockers and OUR HOMES.

It produces ozone. We've talked about

ozone earlier in this book but ozone is probably one of the most misunderstood, hated and loved element in the earth's atmosphere.

Some say it is a harmful gas capable of doing damage to our lungs. Others say it has the potential of being the *greatest natural purifier* we have available to deal with manmade pollutants.

The truth lies in the understanding of the nature of ozone itself, the mechanisms of ozone formation, the nature of the pollution problem that requires a solution and finally, any adverse health effects involved with ozone as compared with other health risks encountered in our modern indoor environments.

Ozone is commonly accepted to be a pollutant associated with large urban areas typified by Los Angles. It is true that ozone is a part of smog, but it is also true that ozone exists outside of the smog environments in even the purest of outdoor environments.

In unpolluted areas, ozone is created by the action of nitrogen oxides and ultraviolet light from the sun with the natural agricultural and animal husbandry sources of methane and even the hydrocarbon compounds of *isoprene* and *terpene* emitted from trees of the forest.

In fact, anywhere in nature that hydrocarbons exist with strong sunlight and moisture, ozone will occur in some quantities. Areas that are considered the most healthy vacation spots in the country have some of the highest levels of naturally occurring ozone.

Ozone is also created electrically in nature during active thunderstorms. The electrical discharge creates that positive sweet smell that we understand as clean fresh air and that we can recall as the fresh smell of laundry hung outside in the sun to dry. Who can deny the positive values associated with sleeping on sheets exposed to and purified by sunlight?

In urban areas ozone is also created in two other important ways. First there is the direct breakdown of chemicals that are spewed into the environment in industrial processes. Formaldehyde, xylene, and olefin also combine with nitrogen oxides and ultraviolet light to create ozone while at the same time reducing the feed stock of these harmful industrial chemicals.

The second is related to the photochemical production of ozone from automobile emissions and mass burners. It can be seen that in the last case that ozone is being created by the breakdown of the hydrocarbons but that it is also aiding in the breakdown of these same chemicals.

It is, therefore, predictable that the highest concentrations of ozone will be found in areas with the highest concentration of *unoxidized or unburned* hydrocarbons. It is this confusion with cause and effect that has given rise to the notion that ozone itself is the source of the problems related to smog rather than just one of the chemicals present in the process.

The additional problem in the air quality of urban areas is related to the magnitude of the feed stocks of unburned hydrocarbons. With heavy industries and the associated heavy automobile traffic, the amount of chemical involved with this process is immense. While the ozone and the hydrocarbons are eliminating each other there are enough of both in the air to be a problem.

As the noted toxicologist Dr. Robert Olcerst wrote in his paper Ozone Monograph: Toxicity and Evaluation, "*Toxicology is the science of poisons. Every chemical substance has a range of effects on biological systems that range from no effect to levels of lethality.*" In effect, every chemical has the capacity to be toxic, and it is dosage that becomes significant. Too much of any substance will upset and become harmful to a biological system.

Ozone is no exception. At extremely high concentrations there are indications that ozone itself is harmful. However, in the case of smog, studies show that its other ingredients, the nitrogen oxides, sulfur oxides, suspended sulfuric acid, nitric acid particles and suspended hydrocarbons are the real health risks.

It is unfortunate that smog and ozone have been interchanged in the discussion of air pollution because it has masked the positive characteristics of ozone as the natural way of dealing with air quality problems. The focus on smog as "air pollution" has prevented us from seeing the even greater problem of indoor air quality problems.

The same chemical soup exists in our indoor environment as exists in smog. The only variant is the concentration of the pollutant and the total lack of any means of reconditioning that air to natural standards. What are the sources of indoor air pollution? The most common sources are:

▶*The building itself and the furnishings in the building emit hazardous chemicals such as formalde-hyde and styrene. Sources range from particle board to ceiling tile to carpets and furniture to paints and finishes.*

▶*Chemicals inadvertently brought into the home such as the residue in dry cleaned clothing, the hydrocarbons collected on our clothing while driving* home, the small amount of chemical residue on the food from the grocer.

▶ *Cleaning products of all types*

▶ *Tobacco smoke and the 3,600 chemicals resulting from that smoke*

▶ *Organic residue from insects, rodents, roaches, pets, etc.*

▶ *Mold, mildew and fungus*

▶ *People themselves! Their sloughed-off skin, their perfumes and toiletries, their food preparation activities, their garbage*

It is interesting to note that most of the pollutants are organic in nature and that the chemicals which we consider to be problems exist all around us in nature where they are not considered problems. To become a problem, as noted earlier, the dosage must be such that adverse effects result.

Dosage is, of course, a function of both concentration and time of exposure. Even small amounts of pollutants will cause adverse effects if the time of exposure is long enough. These adverse effects occur so gradually that they are not associated with their true cause.

The gradually increasing frequency of headaches may never be associated with the move to a new home or the acquisition of new furniture, or a child's allergy problem may not be associated with an exposure to pollutants in the bedroom that began at birth, or the hyperactivity of a child may not be connected to the fact that it began with a subtle change in the environment.

These changes have accelerated since the date of the first oil embargos when the cost of energy for heating and cooling our environments soared. From that date we have attempted to eliminate all outdoor air from our indoor environment. By doing so we have also trapped all of the pollutants indoors and have eliminated the one chemical that has the capacity to restore the air to its pure state—ozone.

Ozone, the most powerful oxidizing agent occurring naturally in our clean outdoor environment, has the capacity to break down most of the organic chemicals that foul our indoor environment.

Ozone is, however, missing from our indoor

environment. Ozone, because of its reactivity must be continually renewed. Ozone concentrations reduce quickly with ozone initially at a concentration of 30 ppb outside totally reverting to oxygen in a period of 20 to 50 minutes depending on a variety of conditions. Unless efforts are made to restore this level in a modern building, the ozone level will normally be zero.

In a study recently commissioned to determine the effect of ozone on chemicals emitted from the opening of returned dry cleaning, the following was determined:

✔ *There is a possibility of 53 chemical substances which are emitted from clothing recently cleaned and stored in air restricting packaging.*

✔ *Fully 2/3 of these chemicals are controlled and regulated by OSHA in industrial settings but not in a home environment.*

✔ *These chemicals may be broken into eight groups, all but one of which react with ozone to form harmless compounds.*

❖ Acids, alcohols, aldehydes, and keytones:
Forms carbon dioxide, water vapor and releases oxygen

❖ Aromatic Compounds such as benzene and camphor):

> Forms carbon dioxide, water vapor and releases oxygen

❖ Liphatic Compounds such as butane and mineral spirits:

> Forms carbon dioxide, water vapor and releases oxygen

❖ Clorines such as methylene chloride:

> Forms carbon dioxide, water vapor, CL^2O and releases oxygen after an intermediate hypochlorite state

❖ Nitrogen Compounds such as Hydrogen Cyanide:

> Forms carbon dioxide, water vapor, and releases nitrogen and oxygen.

❖ Sulphur Compounds such as Ammonium Thiglycolate:

> Forms carbon dioxide, water vapor, sulphur trioxide and releases oxygen (occasionally nitrogen)

❖ Other Alkylated Silicates and non-ionic detergents:

> Forms carbon dioxide and water vapor and release oxygen

❖ Non reactive compounds such as calcium oxide, silica titanium oxides, etc.
No reaction

While these chemicals are not totally *inclusive* of all the chemicals found in the home and work place, they are representative of the families of chemicals that do exist there. As long as pollution levels remain low, small amounts of ozone are sufficient to break them down at a rate that will reduce significantly the exposure rate.

In addition, other tests have shown that common household bacteria, mold, mildew, and fungus are greatly reduced by the addition of as little as 50 ppb in typical household environments. Specifically, E.coli, Salmonella Choleraesuis, Staphylococcus Aureus, Candida Albicans and Aspergillus Niger have been shown to have dramatic reductions.

In a series of studies published in a *Journal Priroda* the Russian Department of Health established a number of important facts concerning the use of ozone in closed indoor environments.

They established that air loses its basic "freshness" quality merely by being drawn into air conditioning and heating systems with as much as 90 percent reduction of the ozone and ion levels.

They established that the effect of the loss of these elements could cause the occupants to complain of headaches, weakness, and a general poor feeling. (What we would identify as *sick building syndrome*.) As a part of the study, they found that after five months of testing with both a test group and a control group, that a feeling of well being returned to those exposed to a level of .15 ppb, and that at these same levels they were able to observe increased immune potential, higher oxygen content in the blood, improved blood pressure reading, and the reduction of many of the stress characteristics associated with working in modern office environments.

They found that by reactivating the air, by the injection of ozone to raise the level to a mere .15 ppb, the overall effect was similar to that of taking an outdoor walk of two hours during the day.

In additional studies done by the Institute of Child and Adolescent Hygiene they concluded that injection of ozone into the air of schools raising the level to .15 ppb had very positive effects on the students. In these tests, 69% of the students exposed to these levels of ozone decreased the

time required to complete tasks requiring high
levels of concentration. In addition, it was found
that favorable changes in the functions of external
respiration, increases in mental reserve capacities,
and overall increases in general state of health
and mental efficiency were observed.

These results agree with the results and
anecdotal testimonies of users of this type of
equipment in this country.

Testimonies show that with the use of this
type of device:

Allergic reactions are reduced.
Sleeping is improved.
Non-specific headaches are reduced.
General poor feeling about the environment
improved.
Depression reduced.
Symptoms of sinus problems relieved.

In general the use of this type of device to
reactivate the air results in the same effect as
being in an outdoor environment in a clean unpolluted part of the world.

With all of these obvious benefits it would
seem that everyone should use this type of device.
It is because sweeping generalization have propa-
gated the myths about the dangers of ozone that

wide acceptance of ozone and its benefits have been ignored.

A study of all of the applicable literature found in the National Library of Medicine's Medline, Toxline, and Toxback database was conducted for Alpine by Dr. Robert Olcerst. The search resulted in over 4,500 documents.

A summary of these documents is as follows:

High and extremely high levels of ozone result in decrements in lung function.

Physiological studies suggest that at these high levels athletes and children may be sensitive to lung functional changes, and that these changes are largely statistical in nature with no visible symptoms.

Tabulation of chamber studies for continuous and intermittent exercise do not indicate lung function decrements of FVC and FEV—I in excess of 10% (the accepted level of criteria of adverse effect) until levels exceed 200 parts-per-billion.

People with lung disorders and with respiratory problems have no more sensitivity to ozone levels than normal people.

There is no indication of adverse effect below 200 ppb

There is no indication that there are any long term effects to prolonged exposure to ozone at levels lower than 120 ppb

Respiratory problems are more affected by other organic pollutants than by ozone, and ozone has the capacity to reduce the levels.

Considering the safety, the wide range and level of effectiveness, the cost of energy and the make up of our current indoor environment it would seem that the closest alternative to opening the window is to replace the vitality of the air by replacing the ozone that occurs naturally outdoors each day.

Chapter 9
TECHNOLOGY—FREE

The GREAT NEWS FOR YOU is that there is a number on the second-to-last-page of this book for you to call to TRY a purifier of the type described in this book in your home—FREE!

If, after THREE DAYS you determine that it has done nothing for you, send it back. They will pay the shipping. NO risk and it DOES work!

There will be someone to talk to who knows WHAT THEY'RE TALKING ABOUT and can answer any questions you might have. As they offered me, they will send you a brochure of the different air purification units and the prices of each.

When you get your unit, follow the instructions to the letter as to where to place the unit (depends on your home of office etc.) and plug it in and turn the dials.

I was excited when I read about this and I did the same as I'm advising you to do.

THE FIRST NIGHT I could tell a difference; I could SMELL the clean air. I tested it as to its power to remove odors and I put some ammonia on my hand and then held it against the front of this little box and in seconds, the ammonia smell was gone.

About two days passed and I called a friend and planned to tell him about the unit. The timing was perfect; a SKUNK (we live in a rural area) had gotten lodged in his ac unit (somehow) UNDER his house and they were getting ready to move to a motel for the evening the smell was so bad. I reached him on his cell phone. He was in his car about to drive off.

"Say no more," I told him. "Stay where you are and I'll be over in minutes with a solution."
I grabbed my XL-15 and drove the two-minutes it took. His wife and two teenage daughters were uneasy and wanted to go.

I went inside and plugged the unit in a wall socket in the living room, and turned both switches on *high*. The skunk was everywhere.

Whether you live in the country or not, if you just drive around in any rural area, chances are you "ran across" a dead skunk in the road and there is nothing like that smell. Imagine what it's like *inside* a home. I thought the skunk was right next to me the smell was so bad. Think about the smell on the furniture and clothes. That smell stays for DAYS.

I took my friend and his family to a local restaurant and we returned to his home in about an hour and a half.

I went inside first (after all, it was my experiment) and he followed close behind. We stood grinning at each other. THE SMELL WAS GONE! He didn't believe it and neither did I. As he shook my hand and hugged me, he called to his wife. "Honey, bring the girls in. The smell is gone!" She didn't believe it and he had to ask a second and then a third time. Reluctantly, three car doors opened and his wife and two daughters emerged—slowly—and sort of tiptoed toward the house. When they came into the living room, they all just smiled and looked at each other. One daughter shrieked in amazement. I didn't shriek but I was amazed also.

With that, I became a believer. With that happening, I decided I'd write a book about it.

Interesting side note: "I wrote a book about 14 years ago titled HOW NOT TO BE LONELY about relationships. The subtitle was: How to find a mate, Where to look, What to say, and How to keep one. Women, being nesters, bought about a thousand to one over men. *Men (hunters not nesters) say, 'We know the answers!'*

"So, to get *men* to buy the book, I did a new cover (same text) and added TONIGHT to the title. Men bought it 400 to 1!

"To make a long story short, the two books sold almost five million copies and I retired. I then decided I needed to do something with my life other than to play golf and vacation and visit exotic places for the rest of my life so I bought a publishing company and published books for other aspiring authors.

"A few years ago I had been playing golf about five days a week for six years when I ran across a fat-loss product that worked on me and my family. I tested it on 144 other people and it worked on 135 of them so I wrote a book about it. I then became more interested in other health matters; I liked helping people feel better.

"When I saw a televison show (either 60 minutes or Peter Jennings) I called around and asked about air purifiers. From the Internet, I ran across *Alpine,* and the rest is history. I have the system, about 30 of my friends and family members have it, and it WORKS! Thus, this book.

"Now, it's your turn to TRY. Call anyone you know who already owns one of these '*Alpines.*' Whatever I know, YOU know because I put it all in this book. I implore each of you to look into this indoor air pollution problem and do something about it, at least in your own home.

"I'm not paranoid. I don't have a microwave diffuser or a burglar alarm on my home. I take some vitamins, I exercise, I give speeches once in a while and I play golf. I also work with new writers but I have enough of those for the next decade so don't send me your manuscript or book. I write for my own enjoyment and only on topics that will help others.

"I don't guess there's much more to say. I'm not embarrassed to admit that I *borrowed* much of the information written in this book because, not being a scientist, I didn't understand it all. I did, however, personally *test* these air purifiers to my own satisfaction. I hope you enjoyed the book; I mean only to do good by it.

"I truly *care* about helping others and that's why I wrote this book. There was a saying a state policemen in South Carolina told me a few years ago and I live by it. *People don't CARE what you KNOW—until they KNOW that you CARE.*"

Pete Billac

THE SILENT KILLER

Indoor Air Pollution

is available through:

Swan Publishing

126 Live Oak
Alvin, TX 77511

(281) 388-2547
Fax (281) 585-3738

or e-mail: swanbooks@ghg.net

Visit our web site at:
http:\\www.swan-pub.com

For additional information call:

www.ecoquestintl.com/charlesminteriors
www.successcycle.com/harnishtech

After reading this book, please pass it on to
a friend or relative. It could change their
lives for the better—FOREVER.

ABOUT THE AUTHOR

PETE BILLAC is one of the most sought-after speakers in the United States. He has written 48 full-length books, hundreds of short stories and he makes his audiences laugh—hard. His worldwide best seller, HOW NOT TO BE LONELY, sold over four million copies.

Pete is a maverick; he writes what pleases him. His topics range from adventure, war, the Mafia, and famous people, to romance, love, health and motivation.

He's given seminars for many Fortune 500 companies on marketing, he lectures at universities across America, and he offers his services free to schools where he speaks about reading and writing. He is also booked for lectures on cruise ships.

Perhaps you've seen Pete on Donahue, Sally Jessy Raphael, Good Morning America, Laff Stop and other national televison shows. He mixes common sense and knowledge with laughter. He charms his audiences, and breathes life into every topic.

"Pete is an expert at restoring self-confidence and self-esteem in others . . ."

Phil Donahue
National Television Talk Show Host